Captain Kind

Lyrics by Mark Collier
Illustrated by Cesar E. De Castro
Painted by Kathy W. Kim and Papo De Asis'
Designed by Barry K. Haun

Published by the Character Building Company
West Covina, California 91791
www.characterbuilding.com
Printed in U.S.A.
ISBN 1-931454-06-X

Library of Congress cataloging-in-publication data is available from the publisher.

Songs in this book are from the **Character Classics** series and are available on cassette and CD.
Coming soon the video series.

Tony Salerno's
Character Classics™
Captain Kind
Created by
Tony Salerno

Captain Kind

The Toreadors from the Opera Carmen - Georges Bizet

Faster than lightning, come to save the day,
Able to chase anger away,
He can stop a fight before it starts,
Turn that bad into good.

A friend to everyone,
A friend of mine,
Hooray for Captain Kind!

Faster than lightning, come to save the day,
Able to chase anger away,
He can stop a fight before it starts,
Turn that bad into good.

A friend to everyone,
A friend of mine,
Hooray for Captain Kind!

Billy the Bully, boy, he's really bad
I've had enough, he makes me mad!
I recall the captain's good advice,
Always best to be kind.

Now Billy has become
A friend of mine,
Hooray for Captain Kind!

My older sister, always on my nerves,
I'll see she gets what she deserves,
Captain to the rescue just in time,
Helping me to be kind!

My sister has become
A friend of mine,
Hooray for Captain Kind!

Faster than lightning, come to save the day,
Able to chase anger away,
He can stop a fight before it starts,
Turn that bad into good.

A friend to everyone,
A friend of mine,
Hooray for Captain Kind!

Faster than lightning, come to save the day,
Able to chase anger away,
He can stop a fight before it starts,
Turn that bad into good.

A friend to everyone,
A friend of mine,
Hooray for Captain Kind!

Always do the kind thing
And remember, kids, don't be afraid to do what's right.
You won't be sorry.
Do kind things for one another.

Now picture this song as you read or sing along...

FASTER THAN LIGHTNING,
COME TO SAVE THE DAY,
ABLE TO CHASE ANGER AWAY,

HE CAN STOP A FIGHT BEFORE IT STARTS,
TURN THAT BAD INTO GOOD.

A FRIEND
TO EVERYONE,

A FRIEND OF MINE,

HOORAY
FOR
CAPTAIN KIND!

FASTER THAN LIGHTNING, COME TO SAVE THE DAY, ABLE TO CHASE ANGER AWAY,
24

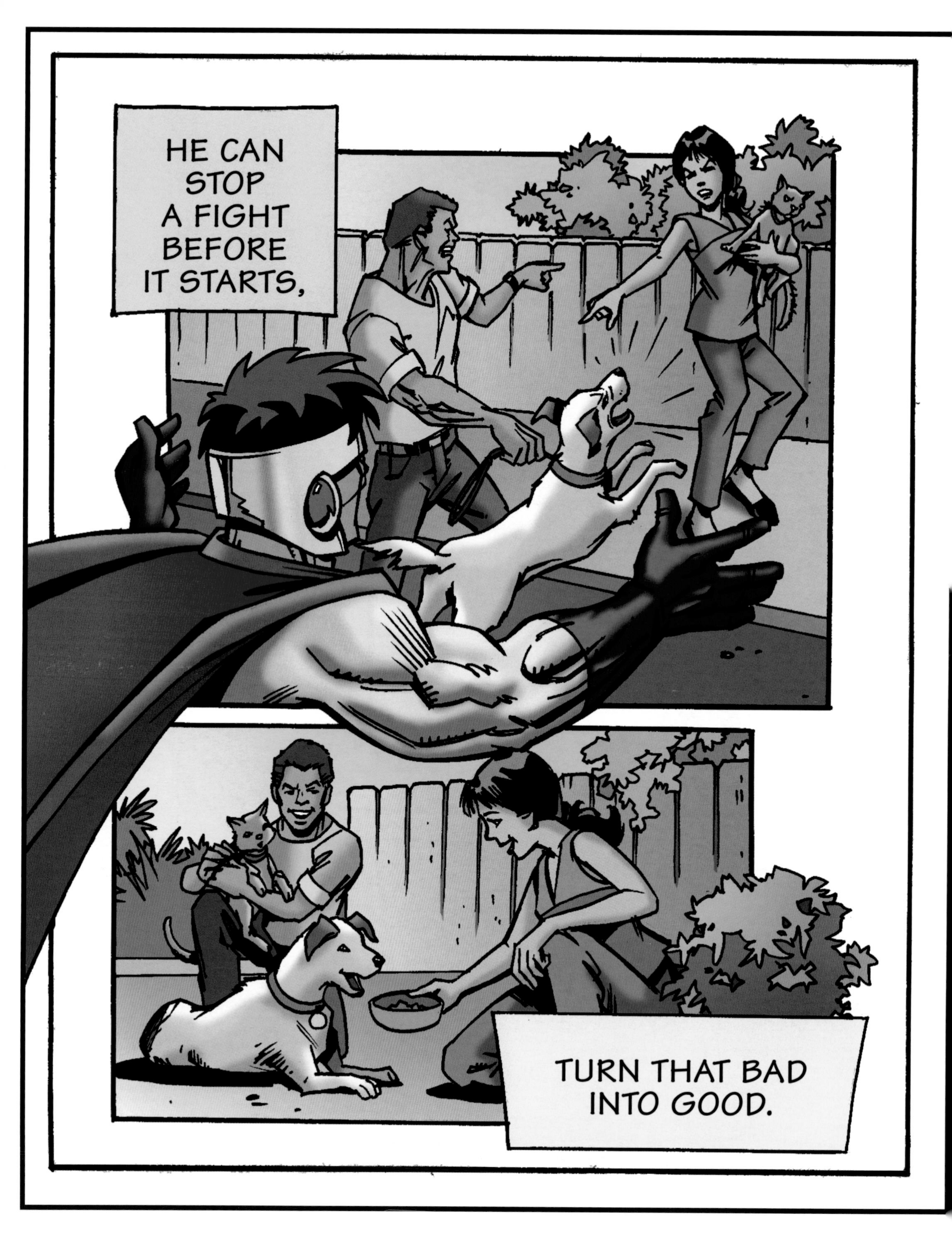
HE CAN STOP A FIGHT BEFORE IT STARTS,
TURN THAT BAD INTO GOOD.

A FRIEND TO EVERYONE,
A FRIEND OF MINE,
HOORAY FOR CAPTAIN KIND!

BILLY THE BULLY, BOY, HE'S REALLY BAD, I'VE HAD ENOUGH, HE MAKES ME MAD!
B
I RECALL THE CAPTAIN'S GOOD ADVICE, ALWAYS BEST TO BE KIND.

NOW BILLY HAS BECOME A FRIEND OF MINE,
HOORAY FOR CAPTAIN KIND!

MY OLDER SISTER, ALWAYS ON MY NERVES, I'LL SEE SHE GETS WHAT SHE DESERVES.

CAPTAIN TO THE RESCUE
JUST IN TIME,
HELPING ME TO BE KIND!

MY SISTER HAS BECOME A FRIEND OF MINE,

HOORAY
FOR CAPTAIN KIND!

FASTER THAN LIGHTNING,
COME TO SAVE THE DAY,
ABLE TO CHASE ANGER AWAY,

HE CAN STOP A FIGHT BEFORE IT STARTS, TURN THAT BAD INTO GOOD.

A FRIEND
TO
EVERYONE,

A FRIEND OF MINE,
HOORAY
FOR CAPTAIN KIND!

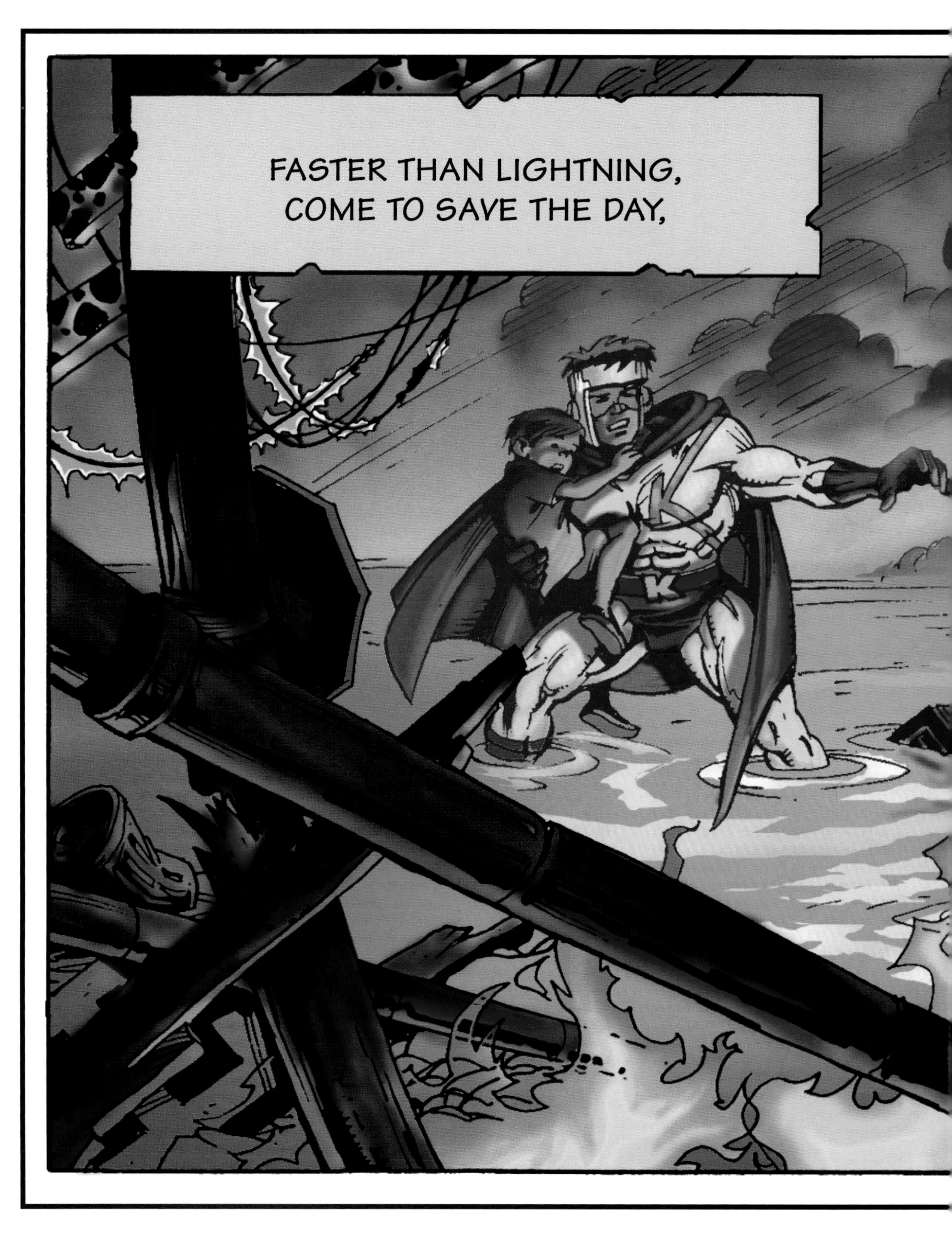
FASTER THAN LIGHTNING,
COME TO SAVE THE DAY,

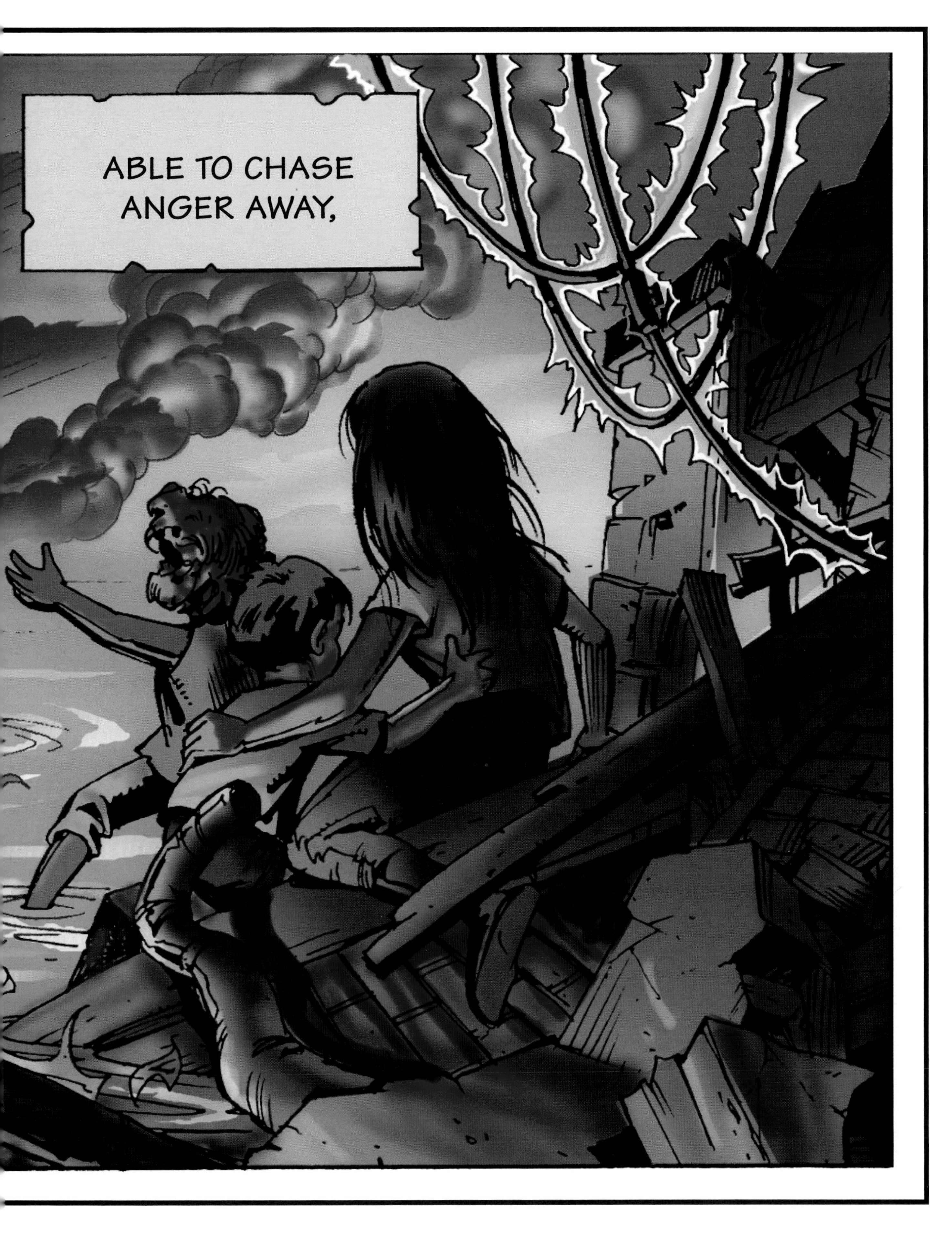
ABLE TO CHASE
ANGER AWAY,

HE CAN STOP A FIGHT BEFORE IT STARTS, TURN THAT BAD INTO GOOD.
YOUTH ORG.
RELIEF CENTER
MILK

A FRIEND TO EVERYONE, A FRIEND OF MINE,
HOORAY
FOR CAPTAIN KIND!
CK

ALWAYS DO
THE KIND THING
AND REMEMBER, KIDS,
DON'T BE AFRAID
TO DO WHAT'S RIGHT.
YOU WON'T BE SORRY.
DO KIND THINGS
FOR ONE ANOTHER.
9

Melody of Kindness

Humoresque No. 7

Antonin Dvorák

When I'm kind, it's plain to see
That others will be kind to me
And that's how I remember to be kind.

If you're kind in what you do,
Then people will be kind to you,
Remember this and you'll be kind.

O do a good deed,
And plant a kind seed!
Let kindness be found all around
And when you share a kind deed
Then you will see
Kindness growing,
Kindness flowing all around!

When I'm kind, it's plain to see
That others will be kind to me
And that's how I remember to be kind.

If you're kind in what you do,
Then people will be kind to you,
Remember this and you'll be kind.

When I'm kind, it's plain to see
That others will be kind to me
And that's how I remember to be kind.

If you're kind in what you do,
Then people will be kind to you,
Remember this and you'll be kind.

When I'm kind, it's plain to see
That others will be kind to me
And that's how I remember to be kind.

If you're kind in what you do,
Then people will be kind to you,
Remember this and you'll be kind.

Duck and Gator

Anna Magdalena Bach Notebook-Musette

Johann Sebastian Bach

Kind alligator, sweet alligator,
Reckon' I'll have myself some dinner.
Nice alligator, dear alligator,
Get me some duckling on my plate.
Big alligator, strong alligator,
One that is plump, not many feathers.
Smart alligator, good alligator,
Over here, duck, don't make me wait!

Beautiful reptile of the swamps,
You are king and I am just a duckling,
You are so quick and clever,
Can't we be friends forever,
All the other animals around will want to be your friend, too.
Is that really true?

Kind alligator, sweet alligator,
What am I going to do for dinner?
Nice alligator, dear alligator,
Guess I'll go back to leaves and sticks.

Beautiful reptile of the swamps,
You are king and I am just a duckling,
You are so quick and clever,
Can't we be friends forever,
All the other animals around will want to be your friend, too.
Is that really true?
I'll be your friend!

Big alligator, strong alligator,
Nobody else has ever liked me,
Smart alligator, good alligator,
Alligator?
Hey, little ducky, let's be friends!

Show a Little Kindness

Spinning Song

Albert Elmenreich

Show a little kindness each day,
In all that you do and say.
Lend a helping hand as you play,
Spread a seed of joy in your way.

And you will bring
Smiles to every face each day
And you'll make the world a better place!

Spread a seed of joy in your way,
Lend a helping hand as you play.
In all that you do and you say,
Show a little kindness each day.

Be a true friend
Through thick and thin
Caring and kind
All of the time.

Make every day
Better some way
Tell all your friends
Kindness will win!

Show a little kindness each day,
In all that you do and say.
Lend a helping hand as you play,
Spread a seed of joy in your way.

And you will bring
Smiles to every face each day
And you'll make the world a better place!

Spread a seed of joy in your way,
Lend a helping hand as you play.
In all that you do and say,
Show a little kindness each day.

I'm Only a Tree

March from The Nutcracker Suite

Peter Tchaikovsky

I'm only a tree, be kind to me,
I'm only a tree, be kind to me.

My name is Pete, I am a pine,
Been standing here the longest time,
I'm big, I'm green, I'm tall, I'm clean,
I want to be your friend.

I'm only a tree, be kind to me,
I'm only a tree, be kind to me.

I smell the best of any tree,
I'll give you all my cones for free,
Don't let them chop me down,
I'm more than just good wood!

I'm only a tree, be kind to me,
I'm only a tree, be kind to me.

My name is Ed, I am an oak,
I'm from a line of friendly folk,
I'm big and strong and beautiful,
I want to be your friend.

I'm only a tree, be kind to me,
I'm only a tree, be kind to me.

I give you shade and oxygen,
My leaves protect you from the wind,
I'm good for climbing, building forts,
Or hang a swing from me.

I'm only a tree, be kind to me,
I'm only a tree, be kind to me.

My name is Paula, I'm a palm,
With other trees I have no qualm,
But I'm as different as can be,
I want to be your friend.

I'm only a tree, be kind to me,
I'm only a tree, be kind to me.

I'm tall and thin with lots of hair,
Sometimes there's coconuts up there,
I don't need much attention,
Just sit back and watch me grow.
I'm only a tree, be kind to me.

Kindness Every Day

Turkish March

Ludwig van Beethoven

Kindness is the golden rule,
Fill up the cup of kindness till it's full.
Share a smile along the way,
Be kind to others every day!

Care a little
Care a lot and
Make this world
A better spot by

Kindness, kindness, every day,
So share a drop of love along the way.
Keep the golden rule each day,
And you will show the world the way!

Fine.

fee´·nay
A musical term for the end.